Amazing Words

Edited By Allanah Jackson-James

First published in Great Britain in 2020 by:

Young Writers
Remus House
Coltsfoot Drive
Peterborough
PE2 9BF
Telephone: 01733 890066
Website: www.youngwriters.co.uk

Printed and bound in the UK by BookPrintingUK
Website: www.bookprintinguk.com
YB0442O

Dear Reader,

Welcome to a fun-filled book of acrostic poems!

Here at Young Writers, we are delighted to introduce our new poetry competition for KS1 pupils, *My First Acrostic: Animal Adventures*. Acrostic poems are an enjoyable way to introduce pupils to the world of poetry and allow the young writer to open their imagination to a range of topics of their choice. The colourful and engaging entry forms allowed even the youngest (or most reluctant) of pupils to create a poem using the acrostic technique and with that, encouraged them to include other literary techniques such as similes and description. Here at Young Writers we are passionate about introducing the love and art of creative writing to the next generation and we love being a part of their journey.

From the jungle to the ocean, pets to mythical monsters, these pupils take you on a journey through the animal kingdom and showcase their budding creativity along the way. So we invite you to dive into these pages and take a glimpse into these blossoming young writers' minds. We hope you will relish these roarsome poems as much as we have.

Contents

Poppy Roberts (6)	58
Ryan Lockett (7)	59
Oliver Critchley (6)	60
Harrison McGowan (7)	61
Ruby Pullen (6)	62
Amelia Dobson (6)	63
Harry Walker (6)	64
Thomas Foster (6)	65
Jack Roby (6)	66

Park View Primary School, Cambuslang

Lleyton Marshall (6)	67
Morgan Mackay (5)	68
Layla Sibbald (5)	69
Sofia Robinson (5) & Scarlet	70
Mark McNeill (5) & Alexus	71
Mia Esin (5)	72
Oliver Rooney (5) & Robyn Anderson (5)	73
Emily Brown (5)	74
Taylor Keenan (5) & Cayson	75
Alfie Keenan (5) & Lucas McIntyre (5)	76
David O'Connor (5)	77
Ellia O'Rourke (5) & Millie	78
Quinn Hutcheson (5)	79
Sophie Masterson (4)	80
Bryony McGregor (5)	81
Olivia Harris (5)	82
Finlay Boardman (5)	83
Isla Best (5)	84

Seaview Primary School, Deneside

Aiden Lisle (7)	85
Ryan Bainbridge (7)	86
Amelia Bampton (6)	87
Hunter Scholes (5)	88
Ella Shotton (6)	89
Max Smith (6)	90
Amelia Hadfield (5)	91

Loui Mather (5)	92
Effie Mae Pattison (5)	93
Nadia Lekka (6)	94
Dougie Grant (7)	95
Martin Kennedy (6)	96
Louie Dunn (6)	97
Jessica Moon (6)	98
Lacey Hadfield (6)	99
Chantelle Boagey (7)	100
Carter Scholes (7)	101
Brooke Stewart (6)	102
Alivia Taylor (5)	103
Harley Ryan (7)	104
Zayne Cole (6)	105
Jack Smith (5)	106
Jake Shepherd (6)	107
Jack Morley (6)	108
Sienna Scott-Fenwick (6)	109
William Lowery (5)	110
Theo Turnbull (5)	111
Megan Miller (6)	112
William Martins (6)	113
Jack Bate (5)	114
Elena James (5)	115

St Barnabas CE Primary Academy, Darwen

Daisy Lewis (6)	116
Jessica Hart (5)	117
Jake Perry (6)	118
Ezmae Haworth (6)	119
Daniel Ridsdale (5)	120
Beau Bentley (5)	121
Jacob Thompson (5)	122
Shaneya Nicol (5)	123
Josh Davies (5)	124
Austin Steele (5)	125
Charlie-Rose Crawshaw (5)	126
Finn Sumner (5)	127
Harry Duce (5)	128

St Paul's CE Primary School, Gloucester

Ricards Savickis (5)	129
Rhys Dearden (5)	130

Worstead CE Primary School, Worstead

Taylor Mitchell (5)	131
Ava Ward (6)	132
Wilfred Wheeler (7)	133
Sammy Day (6)	134
Luther Lewis (6)	135
Ruby Lovewell (6)	136
Daniel Briggs (6)	137
Henry Watson (7)	138
Isla Richardson (7)	139
Thomas Aldus (7)	140
Kyan Allen (6)	141
Imogen Nash (6)	142
Jasmin Bailey (7)	143
Eli Fenwick (6)	144
William Hall (5)	145
Isla Selfe (7)	146
Arabella Gilligan (5)	147
Chloe Jackson (7)	148
Libby Davison (6)	149
Pollyanna Williams (6)	150
Amelia Hart (5)	151
Pip Paterson (5)	152
Finley Blackwell (5)	153

The Poems

Cheeky Monkey

M onkeys say

O ooo, they

N ever leave a tree, they

K now lots about bananas

E *eeeeee!*

Y owling all day long.

Logan (5), Kaiden, Jacob Geere (5), Emie (6), Mia Shrubsole (5), Lilly-Anne & Olivia

Golborne Community Primary School, Golborne

Friendly Unicorn

U nbelievable story I heard today!

N ice girl came to me and this is what she said,

"I t was in the old forest just after ten, a beautiful unicorn

C rossed my way. I gasped

'O h gosh', I stopped and I stared.

R ainbow and sparkly it gave me a grin and soon after that disappeared and I

N ever saw it again."

Aleksandra Grygorowicz (6)

Greenlands Primary School, Darenth

The Unicorn Land

U nique and special.

N ice and sweet.

I see a unicorn flying above me.

C an you feel the magic?

O r are you scared to believe?

R eady for the night so I can dream.

N ice thoughts of the unicorn and me.

Olivia Nelson (5)
Greenlands Primary School, Darenth

Monkey Facts

M ess around a lot.

O nly to be found in the zoo and in the wild.

N aughty and cheeky sometimes.

K icks sometimes.

E very monkey has long arms and legs.

Y oung monkeys ride on their mum's back.

Claudia Costa-Richings (6)

Greenlands Primary School, Darenth

Marley The Monkey

M onkey swings from branch to branch.

O ver treetops.

N ever too low.

K icking his legs as he goes.

E very swing, to and fro.

Y ellow bananas all the way home.

Demi Buckley (7)

Greenlands Primary School, Darenth

Tigers

T heir teeth are big and white.

I f you go near they will bite.

G reat big paws.

E nding with sharp claws.

R eally wild animals.

S o best to stay away.

Mason Hunt (6)

Greenlands Primary School, Darenth

Black And White Zebra

Z ebra, black and white.

E arly in the morning like dynamite.

B lack and white stripes.

R unning far away for a trip.

A cross the world.

Ajay Jeyarajah (7)

Greenlands Primary School, Darenth

Bear

B ig brown bear.
E ats everything around
A nd likes to make a loud sound.
R *oar, roar, roar!*

Levi Shaw (7)

Greenlands Primary School, Darenth

Cheeky Monkey

M ischievous.

O ld.

N oisy.

K ing of the jungle.

E ats bananas.

Y oung.

Mia McMahon (6)
Greenlands Primary School, Darenth

Sleepy Old Owl

O ld little owl.
W ho lived in a tree.
L ittle old owl who loved to sleep.

Gracekelly Varey (5)

Greenlands Primary School, Darenth

Dog

D elightful.
O bedient.
G uardian.

Edi Chiva (6)
Greenlands Primary School, Darenth

Zebra The Best

Z estful is my zebra.
E nergetic is my zebra.
B lack and white is my zebra.
R uns thirty-five miles per hour.
A frican is my zebra.

T otally cool is my zebra.
H erbivore is my zebra.
E ach stripe is unique.

B eautiful is my zebra.
E veryone loves my zebra.
S tripy and smart is my zebra.
T he zebra is the best.

Zayna Ajmi (7)

Knaphill Lower School, Knaphill

Monkey Fun

M onkeys look funny as they swing from the tree.

O oh, ooh, ahh, ahh, are the sounds you'll hear as they're playing free.

N ew mothers carry babies on their backs.

K indness is something they do not lack.

E ating fruit and leaves fallen on the ground.

Y ou should go to the zoo to see them hanging around.

Georgia Green (7)

Knaphill Lower School, Knaphill

Scarlet Macaw

S carlet.

C olourful.

A mazing

R adiant.

L oveable.

E nergetic.

T ranquil.

M embers.

A merican bird found in Peru.

C alm.

A mazon.

W onderful, bright wings.

Scarlett Stone (7)
Knaphill Lower School, Knaphill

All About Monkeys

M onkeys are mischievous.
O rangutans are a type of monkey.
N aughty monkeys are really cute.
K ind is sometimes how monkeys act.
E xtraordinary monkeys are amazing.
Y oung monkeys are cheeky.
S uper animals, right?

Neil Sharma (6)
Knaphill Lower School, Knaphill

Singing Turtle

T o see a turtle is so much fun.

U nusually slow because he can't run.

R acing is really not his thing.

T urtles would rather sit and sing.

L istening to his song is very sweet.

E veryone thinks he's got the beat.

Ella Tompkins (7)
Knaphill Lower School, Knaphill

Adventures Of A Rhino

R ugged.

H erbivore.

I mpressive.

N ot very kind.

O bserved.

C rash - a group of rhinos.

E ndangered.

R are.

O xpeckers like rhinos.

S outh African.

Henry Hall (6)

Knaphill Lower School, Knaphill

The Giraffe

G iant giraffes run.

I n the hot African grasslands.

R eaching for leaves to chew

A nd eat.

F abulous animals.

F luttering their eyelashes.

E very single skin pattern is different.

Anabelle Peters (7)

Knaphill Lower School, Knaphill

Jeffrey The Giraffe

G iant.

I ntelligent.

R ather tall.

A ctive (they only sleep for two hours a day!)

F unny (they do the splits to drink water).

F ast.

E ats leaves.

Abishai Prasad (7)

Knaphill Lower School, Knaphill

Polar Poem

P lease protect
O ur
L ovely
A rctic bears
R isked

B y
E xtinction
A s
R eceding ice threatens
S urvival.

Bailey Ward (7)
Knaphill Lower School, Knaphill

Help The Orangutan

O range.

R ed.

A pe.

N eeds protecting.

G entle.

U p high.

T reetops.

A ll arms and legs.

N ow we must help them.

Hayley Edwards (7)
Knaphill Lower School, Knaphill

Horse

H appily trotting along.
O ver the bumps they go.
R ound the woods and the big trees.
S lowly passing through the streams.
E asily winning the race.

Amy Davies (6)
Knaphill Lower School, Knaphill

Monkey

M ischievous.

O h look, it's a banana!

N uts and fruits.

K ind sometimes, cheeky all the time.

E nergetic.

Y ou're my favourite.

Ria Hirani

Knaphill Lower School, Knaphill

Amazing Unicorns

U nbelievable.

N ever gives up.

I ncredible magic.

C onfident.

O riginal horse.

R ainbow tail and mane.

N oble look.

Jessica Grennan (6)
Knaphill Lower School, Knaphill

Squirrel

S mall.

Q uick.

U nique.

I mpossible.

R ed or grey.

R eally cute.

E ats nuts.

L ives in the trees.

Willow Alefounder (6)
Knaphill Lower School, Knaphill

Elephant

E normous.

L ong trunk.

E ars.

P layful.

H erbivore.

A frican and Asian.

N ever forgets.

T usks.

Oliver Chapman (7)

Knaphill Lower School, Knaphill

Koalas Cute Poem

K oalas are cute.

O verlooking Australia.

A koala's joey is the size of a jelly bean.

L iving in trees

A nd eating leaves.

Grace Simmons (7)

Knaphill Lower School, Knaphill

Cheetahs

C hase.

H ide.

E ating.

E nergetic.

T errifying.

A crobatic.

H ungry.

S peedy.

Evie Seager (7)
Knaphill Lower School, Knaphill

Elephant

E ars.

L arge.

E normous.

P owerful.

H eavy.

A frica.

N ice.

T runk and tusks.

Isabelle Rees (6)
Knaphill Lower School, Knaphill

Spiders

S cary.

P owerful.

I nnocent.

D ark black.

E ight legs and evil.

R apid walk.

S pooky.

Yuvraj Choudhary (6)
Knaphill Lower School, Knaphill

Gentle Giant

G iant neck.

I ncredible.

R eally cool.

A frican.

F unny.

F riendly.

E legant.

Annie Alderton (6)
Knaphill Lower School, Knaphill

Cool Cats

C urious cats like to explore.
A ttitude - cats think they rule.
T ricky characters.
S cratch with sharp claws.

Zoe Roulston (6)
Knaphill Lower School, Knaphill

The Delicate Dolphin

D elicate.

O h so playful.

L ovely.

P layful.

H ilarious.

I ncredible.

N ice.

Amelie Bidgood (7)
Knaphill Lower School, Knaphill

Eagle

E xtra-large birds.
A lways in flight.
G reat big wings.
L ike a plane.
E very day flying high.

Jack Eagles (7)

Knaphill Lower School, Knaphill

Unicorn

U nique.

N ature.

I ndividual.

C ute.

O riginal.

R are.

N o one can see.

Jasmin Bogi Hollo (7)
Knaphill Lower School, Knaphill

Funky Monkey

M unching bananas.
O range fur.
N ever still.
K ind.
E ntertaining.
Y ells loudly.

Olivia Cole (7)
Knaphill Lower School, Knaphill

My Rabbit

R ed eyes.

A ctive.

B ouncy.

B ig ears.

I nteresting.

T remendously beautiful.

Ariyanna Tyson (6)
Knaphill Lower School, Knaphill

Cheetah

C arnivore.

H uge.

E nergetic.

E xotic.

T ough.

A ctive.

H airy.

Chloe Fletcher (7)

Knaphill Lower School, Knaphill

Tigers

T erritorial.

I ntelligent.

G olden.

E nergetic.

R oars.

S tripy.

Lillie Hughes (7)

Knaphill Lower School, Knaphill

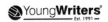

My Puppy Poppy

P layful.

U nbelievable.

P erfect.

P retty puppy who is

Y oung, my Poppy.

Cerys Farmer (6)
Knaphill Lower School, Knaphill

Panda

P aws.
A dventurous.
N ibbling on bamboo.
D angerous.
A nimal.

Amelia Alanson (7)
Knaphill Lower School, Knaphill

Tiger

T alented.

I ntelligent.

G reat.

E ats.

R oars loud.

Ethan Beck (6)

Knaphill Lower School, Knaphill

Puppy

P layful.

U tterly cute.

P ouncing.

P uppy.

Y aps.

Ellie Winn (6)

Knaphill Lower School, Knaphill

Dogs Are The Best

D ogs are loving.

O utstanding.

G uardians.

S oft and cuddly.

Lewis Ahmic (6)

Knaphill Lower School, Knaphill

Crazy Cat

C razy, cuddly, cute.
A dorable, amazing.
T otally terrific.

Ivy Rose Van Goeverden (6)
Knaphill Lower School, Knaphill

The Lion In The Wild

L arge.

I nteresting.

O versized cat.

N oisy.

Oscar Locke (7)
Knaphill Lower School, Knaphill

Dogs

D ecent.

O utstanding.

G uardian.

S mart.

Mounir Hashem (7)
Knaphill Lower School, Knaphill

My Dog Dolly

D ashing.
O bedient.
G rateful.

Caitlin Farmer (6)
Knaphill Lower School, Knaphill

My Polar Bear Poem

P olar bears live in the Arctic.
O n land we are the biggest hunters.
L ong hairs on our feet to stop us slipping.
A lways hunting for seals.
R olling on the snow.

B aby polar bears cuddle with their mum to keep warm.
E ating seals is my favourite.
A t the sea, we swim.
R unning on the ice.

Lily Buckley (7)
Legh Vale Primary School, Haydock

Polar Bears Poem

P olar bears live in the Arctic.
O n land, we are the biggest hunters.
L ong hairs on our feet.
A lways hunting for seals.
R olling on the floor.

B aby bears stay with their mum.
E ating seals is what we do.
A nd sharp claws to dig dens.
R ushing on the ice.

Fearne Rattigan (6)

Legh Vale Primary School, Haydock

My Penguin Poem

P enguins live in the Arctic.

E ating krill and fish.

N ot flying but cuddling.

G liding and sliding on the snow.

U nder the sea they catch fish and krill.

I n a huddle we watch.

N o cold feathers, they are black, white and yellow.

S lowly I tap my webbed feet.

Heidi Critchley (6)
Legh Vale Primary School, Haydock

My Arctic Poem

P olar bears live in the Arctic.
O n the cracking ice.
L iving in the cold Arctic.
A meal for me to eat.
R oaming around the snowy hills.

B aby bears start off small.
E ating seals we like to do.
A n adventure is going on.
R unning to seals.

Daniel Mitchinson (6)
Legh Vale Primary School, Haydock

My Arctic Fox Poem

A bushy tail with white fur.
R ound black nose.
C old and snowy weather I love
T heir claws are very short.
I like to eat lemmings.
C amouflager.

F ind me in the white snow.
O n the ice, it's very cold.
X marks the spot for my food.

Mason Comiskey (6)

Legh Vale Primary School, Haydock

My Penguin Poem

P enguins live in the Arctic.
E ating fish, krill and squid.
N ot flying but swimming to eat my food.
G liding on the cold ice.
U nder the waves, swimming fast.
I n a huddle we waddle.
N o wings to fly.
S lowly waddle.

Emily Woods (6)

Legh Vale Primary School, Haydock

My Penguin Poem

P enguins live in the Arctic.

E ating fish I like the most.

N ot flying but swimming to eat my food.

G liding on the ice is fun.

U nderwater I dive.

I have blubber underneath my skin.

N ot eating people but eating food.

Kortnee Finch (6)

Legh Vale Primary School, Haydock

Penguin

P enguins live in the Arctic.

E ating fish I like the most.

N ot flying but swimming to eat my food.

G liding over the snow.

U nder the sea getting my food.

I swim deep under the water.

N ow I have waterproof feathers.

Elizabeth Porter (6)

Legh Vale Primary School, Haydock

My Penguin Poem

P enguins live in the Arctic.
E ating fish, krill and squid.
N o wings to fly.
G liding on the snow.
U nder the waves, swimming fast.
I n a huddle, we walk.
N ot walking fast.
S lowly tapping my webbed feet.

Jessica Anders (7)

Legh Vale Primary School, Haydock

My Polar Bear Poem

P olar bears live in the Arctic.
O n the snow walking.
L and is snowy.
A rctic is cold.
R iding on snowmobiles.

B y the ice.
E ating fish and krill.
A rctic is icy.
R iding on dog sledges.

Poppy Roberts (6)
Legh Vale Primary School, Haydock

My Penguin Story

P enguins live in the Arctic.
E at fish and krill.
N ot flying but swimming to eat my food.
G liding on the snow and ice.
U nderwater I can swim.
I have a yellow bill.
N o toes but webbed feet.

Ryan Lockett (7)
Legh Vale Primary School, Haydock

Penguin Poem

P enguins live in the Arctic.
E ating fish I like the most.
N ot flying but swimming to eat my food.
G liding on the ice.
U nderwater I swim.
I have webbed feet.
N eed to fly but too full.

Oliver Critchley (6)

Legh Vale Primary School, Haydock

My Penguin Poem

P enguins live in the Arctic.
E ating fish I like the most.
N ot flying but swimming to eat my food.
G lide on the ice.
U nderwater I dive.
I ce is my favourite.
N eed food for my baby.

Harrison McGowan (7)
Legh Vale Primary School, Haydock

My Penguin Poem

P enguins live in the Arctic.
E ating fish I like the most.
N ot flying but swimming to eat my food.
G lide on the ice.
U nderwater I dive.
I ce is my favourite.
N eed food to eat.

Ruby Pullen (6)
Legh Vale Primary School, Haydock

My Penguin Poem

P enguins live in the Arctic.

E ating fish I like.

N ot flying but swimming to eat my food.

G liding on the ice.

U nderwater I can swim.

I swim to get my food.

N ot a black beak.

Amelia Dobson (6)

Legh Vale Primary School, Haydock

My Penguin Poem

P enguins live in the Arctic.
E ating fish I like the most.
N ot flying but swimming to eat my food.
G lide on the ice.
U nderwater I swim.
I can waddle.
N o gaps in their feet.

Harry Walker (6)

Legh Vale Primary School, Haydock

My Penguins Poem

P enguins live in the Antarctic.
E ating fish.
N ot flying but swimming.
G lide on the snow.
U nderwater I dive.
I have webbed feet.
N ot walking but waddling.

Thomas Foster (6)
Legh Vale Primary School, Haydock

My Seal Poem

S eals live in the Arctic and Antarctic.
E at and swim for fish.
A t the Arctic, they hide from predators.
L ove to swim in the cold ice water.

Jack Roby (6)
Legh Vale Primary School, Haydock

Mouse

M ini.

O n cheese.

U nder the table.

S mall.

E xtraordinary.

Lleyton Marshall (6)
Park View Primary School, Cambuslang

Sheep

S illy.
H yper.
E xcited.
E nergetic.
P retty.

Morgan Mackay (5)
Park View Primary School, Cambuslang

Sheep

S illy.

H yper.

E nergetic.

E xcited.

P retty.

Layla Sibbald (5)
Park View Primary School, Cambuslang

Sheep

S illy.

H appy.

E nergetic.

E xcited.

P retty.

Sofia Robinson (5) & Scarlet
Park View Primary School, Cambuslang

Sheep

S illy.

H op.

E xcited.

E nergetic.

P retty.

Mark McNeill (5) & Alexus

Park View Primary School, Cambuslang

Lion

L ively.
I n the zoo.
O n the rocks.
N ice.

Mia Esin (5)
Park View Primary School, Cambuslang

Lion

L ovely.

I ncredible.

O range.

N ice.

Oliver Rooney (5) & Robyn Anderson (5)

Park View Primary School, Cambuslang

Lion

L ovely.
I n the zoo.
O range.
N ice.

Emily Brown (5)
Park View Primary School, Cambuslang

Duck

D iving.
U nderwater.
C ute.
K ind.

Taylor Keenan (5) & Cayson
Park View Primary School, Cambuslang

Duck

D iving.
U mbrella.
C ute.
K ing.

Alfie Keenan (5) & Lucas McIntyre (5)

Park View Primary School, Cambuslang

Cat

C arnivore

F ast cat

T errifying.

David O'Connor (5)

Park View Primary School, Cambuslang

Cat

C uddly.

A dorable.

T errific.

Ellia O'Rourke (5) & Millie

Park View Primary School, Cambuslang

Cat

C laws.
A dorable.
T errific.

Quinn Hutcheson (5)

Park View Primary School, Cambuslang

Cat

C ute.
A dorable.
T errific.

Sophie Masterson (4)

Park View Primary School, Cambuslang

Cat

C ute
A dorable
T errifying.

Bryony McGregor (5)
Park View Primary School, Cambuslang

Pig

P ink.

I nteresting.

G ood.

Olivia Harris (5)

Park View Primary School, Cambuslang

Dog

D irty.

O ld.

G rumpy.

Finlay Boardman (5)

Park View Primary School, Cambuslang

Dog

D irty.
O ld.
G reat.

Isla Best (5)

Park View Primary School, Cambuslang

Giraffe

G iraffes are my favourite animals.

I n Africa, you will find them.

R eally long necks help them eat.

A nd they can reach right to the top of the trees.

F or about twenty-five years on average, they live for.

F eeding and scavenging can take up to seventy-five percent of their day.

E very giraffe has spots that are unique.

Aiden Lisle (7)

Seaview Primary School, Deneside

Dini The Dinosaur

D inosaurs come in different sizes.

I n fact, some have very long necks.

N ana Linda is prehistoric!

O ut in the prehistoric age, a long time ago.

S tegosaurus is my favourite dinosaur

A nd tyrannosaurus. However, I would hide

U nder a rock or hole, so I would not hear them

R oar!

Ryan Bainbridge (7)

Seaview Primary School, Deneside

Elephant

E xtremely big and grey.

L ying asleep sometime today.

E ating small plants and also spiders.

P redators, lions and tigers.

H air on their heads to keep them cool.

A lso known as a gentle giant.

N oise like a trumpet, that's what we think.

T runk to help them eat and drink.

Amelia Bampton (6)

Seaview Primary School, Deneside

About A Rabbit

R abbits have fluffy cottontails.
A nd they love to jump and hoppity-hop.
B ig ears they have, as soft as silk.
B ig, crunchy carrots they love to eat.
I n the ground, they dig their burrows.
T witchy twitch, they do with their nose.

Hunter Scholes (5)
Seaview Primary School, Deneside

Enormous Elephant

E normously large.

L ong trunk and sprays water.

E ats fruit and tree bark.

P lays in the water.

H ome is a jungle or zoo.

A fraid of bees.

N ever forgets.

T usks are very strong.

Ella Shotton (6)

Seaview Primary School, Deneside

Elephant

E lephants are land mammals.

L arge and grey.

E ating plants, grass and fruit.

P ick up food with the trunk.

H ave good memories.

A re very emotional.

N o meat eating.

T runk.

Max Smith (6)
Seaview Primary School, Deneside

Magical Unicorns

U nique in their own way.

N ame is so different.

I love unicorns.

C arries happiness to animals.

O dd in a good way.

R ainbows are their best friends.

N o one thinks they're real.

Amelia Hadfield (5)

Seaview Primary School, Deneside

Monkey

M onkeying around is what I do.
O ver here is where I hide from you!
N o one knows how I feel.
K ing of the jungle, people say.
E ver so hairy, even in May.
Y es, I am a monkey. I like to play.

Loui Mather (5)
Seaview Primary School, Deneside

Giraffe

G iant hooves for walking on sand.
I sleep standing up.
R unning is what I like to do.
A frica is where I live.
F eeding on trees and leaves.
F emales are called cows.
E ndangered.

Effie Mae Pattison (5)
Seaview Primary School, Deneside

Zebra

Z ebras are from Africa.

E thiopia is the place where they live.

B lack and white stripes have.

R anging in seven countries.

A s elegant and peaceful they are, they can be aggressive.

Nadia Lekka (6)

Seaview Primary School, Deneside

Penguin

P enguins are black and white.

E ggs hatch a chick.

N ew babies are cold.

G liding on ice.

U nder the mummy's wing.

I n ice and snow.

N ice and fluffy.

Dougie Grant (7)

Seaview Primary School, Deneside

Charlie The Monkey

M y monkey Charlie is as clever as can be.

O n the hunt for bananas.

N oisy in the trees.

K ind at heart.

E xtraordinary animal.

Y ou can find him in the rainforest.

Martin Kennedy (6)

Seaview Primary School, Deneside

My Dragons

D ragons are mystical.

R iding high in the sky.

A wesome fire breathers.

G igantic, scaly wings.

O range is a colour they can be.

N ot really seen but we can dream.

Louie Dunn (6)
Seaview Primary School, Deneside

My Favourite Animal

Z oo is the place where I live.
E ating leaves and grass is what I like.
B lack and white stripes are what I have.
R unning around is what I do.
A frica is where I was born.

Jessica Moon (6)
Seaview Primary School, Deneside

Zoe The Zebra

Z ebra, zebra, black and white.
E arly morning, dark of night.
B eware the mighty lion's bite.
R un, run, run with all your might.
A way, away, get out of sight.

Lacey Hadfield (6)

Seaview Primary School, Deneside

Unicorn

U nhappy unicorn
N o friends at all
I n the city
C atching a hairy ball
O nly I can see her
R unning in the grass
N ever looking back.

Chantelle Boagey (7)
Seaview Primary School, Deneside

Facts About Sharks

S harks live in every ocean.
H ave fins to help them swim.
A ir they breathe through their gills.
R azor-sharp teeth they have.
K ing or queen of the sea.

Carter Scholes (7)

Seaview Primary School, Deneside

Nocturnal Masked Bandits

R acoons are awesome.

A lso wears a mask.

C limbing in trees.

O mnivores, they are.

O nly come out at night.

N octurnal masked bandits.

Brooke Stewart (6)
Seaview Primary School, Deneside

Rabbit

R abbits are different colours.

A re fluffy and cuddly.

B ucktoothed.

B lack nose.

I n burrows, they live.

T hey love to jump around.

Alivia Taylor (5)

Seaview Primary School, Deneside

Ruben Rabbit

R uben is my pet
A nd is black.
B ig and fluffy.
B ecause I need to feed him
I need to look after him.
T he cage needs cleaning.

Harley Ryan (7)
Seaview Primary School, Deneside

Lion

L ions are the meanest predators.
I n the jungle, the lion is king.
O ld lions fight young lions to be king.
N o animal is as cool as a lion.

Zayne Cole (6)
Seaview Primary School, Deneside

Dog

D ogs are a man's best friend.

O bviously my dog, Roxy, is the best dog in the world.

G oing for walks is her favourite thing to do. I love her.

Jack Smith (5)
Seaview Primary School, Deneside

Lizard

L ong, slippery tongue.
I n the trees.
Z esty.
A ctive.
R oaming.
D eadly silent, waiting for prey.

Jake Shepherd (6)
Seaview Primary School, Deneside

A Shark's Tale

S wimming in the water.
H unting for prey.
A ggressive and big.
R eally fast at swimming.
K ing of the sea.

Jack Morley (6)
Seaview Primary School, Deneside

Zebra

Z ebras are white and black.
E asy to spot.
B old and brave.
R unning like the wind
A long with the snail.

Sienna Scott-Fenwick (6)
Seaview Primary School, Deneside

Hippo

H as large jaws.
I n Africa.
P lants are what they eat.
P lay with the baby hippos.
O ne muddy hippo.

William Lowery (5)
Seaview Primary School, Deneside

Fish

F ish live in water.

I ncredible swimmers.

S limy and scaly.

H as lots of different friends.

Theo Turnbull (5)

Seaview Primary School, Deneside

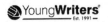
My Dream Dog Friend

P etite and cuddly like a squishy.
U p to mischief like the elf.
G ooey and dribbles like my brother.

Megan Miller (6)
Seaview Primary School, Deneside

My Dog Coco

D ogs are fun.
O range is its colour.
G ood girl, Coco.
S ee her run!

William Martins (6)
Seaview Primary School, Deneside

Dog

D ogs like to go on big walks.
O nly like to eat dog food.
G reat friends.

Jack Bate (5)

Seaview Primary School, Deneside

Cat

C ats go, "Meow."
A lways sleeping and snuggling.
T oy chasers.

Elena James (5)

Seaview Primary School, Deneside

Tigers

T igers are dangerous.

I nside their eyes is fire.

G rowling sometimes.

E ach step they take they're watching their prey.

R unning very fast through the jungle.

Daisy Lewis (6)

St Barnabas CE Primary Academy, Darwen

Horse

H ay is the food.
O ver the fence, they jump.
R unning in the field.
S ome sleep in the stables.
E ating all of the grass.

Jessica Hart (5)
St Barnabas CE Primary Academy, Darwen

Tiger

T hey catch their prey.

I n the wild.

G reat, sharp, sparkly teeth.

E yes are on fire.

R uns through the jungle.

Jake Perry (6)
St Barnabas CE Primary Academy, Darwen

118

Horse

H ave hay to eat.

O n the grass.

R unning on the grass.

S ome gallop.

E ating the grass in the field.

Ezmae Haworth (6)

St Barnabas CE Primary Academy, Darwen

Horse

H ay is their food.
O ver the fence.
R aces quickly.
S hooting up.
E xcited to gallop.

Daniel Ridsdale (5)
St Barnabas CE Primary Academy, Darwen

Cat

C laws as sharp as glass.
A re good at scratching.
T hey are jumpers.
S cratch with their claws.

Beau Bentley (5)
St Barnabas CE Primary Academy, Darwen

Dogs

D ig with their paws.
O verexcited when they play.
G ood at barking.
S leeping in their bed.

Jacob Thompson (5)
St Barnabas CE Primary Academy, Darwen

Cats

C ats drink milk.

A nimals have sharp claws.

T hey can scratch!

S it down on the bed.

Shaneya Nicol (5)

St Barnabas CE Primary Academy, Darwen

Cats

C laws are sharp.
A re good at jumping.
T hinking of milk.
S cratch with their claws.

Josh Davies (5)
St Barnabas CE Primary Academy, Darwen

Dogs

D o have floppy ears.

O verexcited.

G rowl and snarl.

S uper careful with his ball.

Austin Steele (5)

St Barnabas CE Primary Academy, Darwen

Dogs

D ogs eat food.

O verexcited.

G reat friends.

S cratching the doors to get out.

Charlie-Rose Crawshaw (5)

St Barnabas CE Primary Academy, Darwen

Dogs

D ogs fetch balls.

O verexcited.

G naw and snore.

S uper at playing fetch.

Finn Sumner (5)

St Barnabas CE Primary Academy, Darwen

Dogs

D ogs eat meat.
O verexcited.
G et down!
S leeping on a bed.

Harry Duce (5)
St Barnabas CE Primary Academy, Darwen

Giraffe

G iraffe is orange and spotty.

I t has a long neck and four legs.

R iding on it is impossible.

A s a giraffe is not a pet.

F riendly looking.

F ace is like a triangle.

E ating leaves from the trees.

Ricards Savickis (5)

St Paul's CE Primary School, Gloucester

Dino Poem

D angerous.

I nteresting.

N ice.

O ld.

S cary.

A wesome.

U nique.

R eptiles.

Rhys Dearden (5)
St Paul's CE Primary School, Gloucester

Butterfly

B utterflies fly quickly towards the flower.

U nder the ground, they sleep.

T he butterfly flies, hey, hey! Come and play.

T he butterfly was sprinting through the sky.

E verywhere they fly, they leave glitter.

R un, run, little butterfly, before it eats you.

F ly quickly, before you get wet.

L ovely butterfly glowing in the dark.

Y ou are a wonderful little butterfly.

Taylor Mitchell (5)
Worstead CE Primary School, Worstead

Tortoise

T ortoise eats greens.

O ld ones plod slowly.

R ests in cold, dirty water.

T hey are amazing at hide-and-seek.

O nly excited ones jump out of their glittery shells!

I love the cute ones.

S lowly, slowly tiptoe.

E very day, they hang out in the water.

Ava Ward (6)
Worstead CE Primary School, Worstead

Spiders

S cary spiders creep slowly in the night.

P ounce on flies and put them in a web.

I nteresting, cool spiders in the dark, spooky woods.

D angerous spiders that bite and crawl.

E ven other insects can't beat it at all.

R avenous beasts, so mean and they are quick.

Wilfred Wheeler (7)

Worstead CE Primary School, Worstead

Gorilla

G orillas thump their chests quickly to scare people away.

O ctopuses hate gorillas.

R ude gorilla throws bananas at people.

I love gorillas.

L ively gorillas can hurt you a lot.

L iving in the comfortable treetops.

A nimals are the best!

Sammy Day (6)

Worstead CE Primary School, Worstead

Pandas

P andas plodding through the bamboo forest slowly.

A lways munch and crunch on awesome bamboo.

N ever mess with pandas because you might get a shock.

D on't go near baby pandas.

A ll day, all night, pandas roll all through the gold and black night.

Luther Lewis (6)

Worstead CE Primary School, Worstead

Butterfly

B utterflies like to fly to the park
U nder the sky
T hey love to play along
T hey flutter in the sky
E veryone played with the butterfly
R ed and green
F lutter and fly
L ovely butterfly
Y ou are the best.

Ruby Lovewell (6)
Worstead CE Primary School, Worstead

Snake

S limy, scaly snake in the neat, tidy and green grass.

N obody approaches the deadly snake.

A lways deadly, day and night.

K illing a cuddly, cute rabbit and eventually eating it.

E verywhere you go in the night, beware of the slithery snake.

Daniel Briggs (6)
Worstead CE Primary School, Worstead

Parrot

P arrots pick on cheeky gorillas.

A mazing attitude and very cheeky.

R acing away from hunters.

R eady to fly into the turquoise sky.

O nly one thing to do - fly away into the sunlight.

T ingly, tangly, tickly parrot.

Henry Watson (7)
Worstead CE Primary School, Worstead

Koala

K oalas climb up big, fancy trees.
O ne cheeky koala eats all the eucalyptus leaves.
A dorable, cuddly and cute koalas love to cuddle you.
L ovely koalas love to drink from the lake.
A dventurous koalas love to climb everywhere.

Isla Richardson (7)
Worstead CE Primary School, Worstead

Skunk

S mellier than a sock and deadly as a devil.

K illing lovely plants and letting them die.

U p to no good, nothing can stop it.

N ever go near one or you will get a surprise!

K eeps waddling about slowly, looking for a lizard.

Thomas Aldus (7)
Worstead CE Primary School, Worstead

Gorilla

G orillas are grey.

O ctopuses don't like gorillas.

R ubbing on trees.

I love gorillas.

L ions chase gorillas.

L iving in the beautiful forest.

A mazing gorillas love bananas.

Kyan Allen (6)
Worstead CE Primary School, Worstead

Panda

P erfect, pretty panda.

A dorable, cuddly panda. They eat too much.

N o more bamboo, panda, you ate too much!

D ay and night eating delicious food.

A lways hiding in the green bushes.

Imogen Nash (6)

Worstead CE Primary School, Worstead

Horse

H ard-working horses trotting around the field.

O nly eating dry, yummy hay.

R acehorses are fast.

S melly, silly, wet horses out in the rain.

E legantly prancing around in a circle.

Jasmin Bailey (7)

Worstead CE Primary School, Worstead

Wolf

W ild, deadly and dangerous, with sharp, pointy teeth.
O nly eating fluffy, white sheep.
L oud, mean, nasty.
F urious and vicious, they might give you a fright!

Eli Fenwick (6)
Worstead CE Primary School, Worstead

Spider

S pider has six eyes.

P uts webs everywhere.

I t can jump.

D angerously, they kill over one hundred people.

E verybody is

R eally scared.

William Hall (5)

Worstead CE Primary School, Worstead

Cats

C ats are soft and cuddly.

A dorable cats drink yummy, scrumptious milk.

T he cat chases cheeky mice.

S oft cats make you feel sleepy.

Isla Selfe (7)
Worstead CE Primary School, Worstead

Deer

D eers like to play every day.

E ating orange and green carrots.

E veryone can see them fly.

R eindeers are really fluffy and smooth.

Arabella Gilligan (5)

Worstead CE Primary School, Worstead

Cat

C ats creep quietly and pounce on a
mouse.
A lways trying to catch frightened birds.
T errible, terrifying, prowling in the night.

Chloe Jackson (7)

Worstead CE Primary School, Worstead

Dogs

D ogs chase balls crazily.
O ver the field, they run.
G ood dogs sitting on your lap.
S oft dogs are cute and cuddly.

Libby Davison (6)
Worstead CE Primary School, Worstead

Cat

C ute cats chasing naughty mice fearlessly.
A naughty cat bit and scratched me.
T wo clumsy cats fighting together.

Pollyanna Williams (6)
Worstead CE Primary School, Worstead

Dog

D izzy, dangerous dogs like to sleep
O n their owner's lap.
G ood, yummy treats.

Amelia Hart (5)
Worstead CE Primary School, Worstead

Pony

P ony eats hay.
O n my own to ride.
N ose is soft.
Y es, carrots.

Pip Paterson (5)
Worstead CE Primary School, Worstead

Dog

D ogs like to run.

O n the lead.

G oing fast.

Finley Blackwell (5)

Worstead CE Primary School, Worstead

Young Writers
Est. 1991

Young Writers Information

We hope you have enjoyed reading this book – and that you will continue to in the coming years.

If you're a young writer who enjoys reading and creative writing, or the parent of an enthusiastic poet or story writer, do visit our website **www.youngwriters.co.uk**. Here you will find free competitions, workshops and games, as well as recommended reads, a poetry glossary and our blog. There's lots to keep budding writers motivated to write!

If you would like to order further copies of this book, or any of our other titles, then please give us a call or order via your online account.

Young Writers
Remus House
Coltsfoot Drive
Peterborough
PE2 9BF
(01733) 890066
info@youngwriters.co.uk

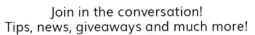

Join in the conversation!
Tips, news, giveaways and much more!

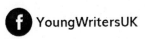 YoungWritersUK

 @YoungWritersCW